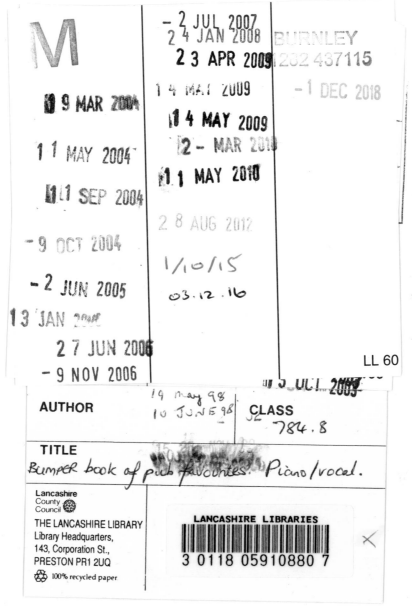

BUMPER BOOK OF
PUB FAVOURITES

Edited by PETER FOSS

First Published 1988
© EMI Music Publishing Ltd
138 Charing Cross Road, London WC2H 0LD

Exclusive Distributors
International Music Publications
Southend Road, Woodford Green,
Essex IG8 8HN, England.

18.95

BUMPER BOOK OF
PUB FAVOURITES

CONTENTS

BUMPER BOOK OF
PUB FAVOURITES

CONTENTS

APRIL SHOWERS

Words by B G DE SILVA
Music by LOUIS SILVERS

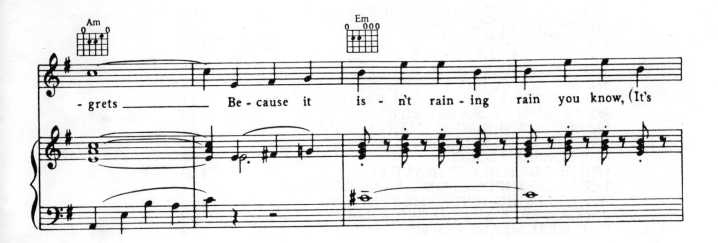

rain - ing vi - o - lets,) And where you see clouds ___ up - on the hills, ___

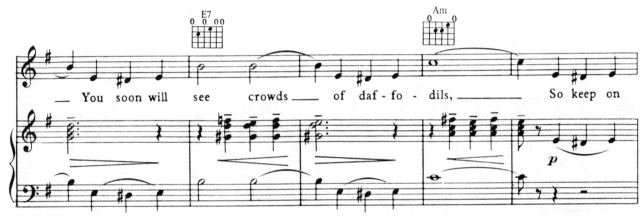

___ You soon will see crowds ___ of daf - fo - dils, ___ So keep on

look - ing for a blue - bird And list - 'ning for his song, When - ev - er A - pril

show - ers come a - long. ___ Though A - pril - long. ___

AFTER THE BALL

Words and Music
by CHAS K HARRIS

AT TRINITY CHURCH

Words and Music
by FRED GILBERT

BILL BAILEY

Words and Music
by HUGHIE CANNON

rain - y eve - ning I drove you out with noth - ing but a fine tooth comb (a fine tooth comb) I know I'm to blame well ain't that a shame? Bill Bail - ey won't you please come home home.

BLESS 'EM ALL

Words by FRANK LAKE
Music by JIMMY HUGHES

CHORUS

BLESS 'EM ALL! BLESS 'EM ALL! The long and the short and the tall,

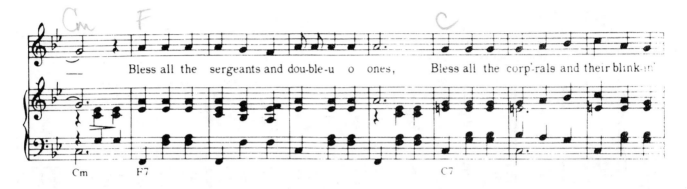

Bless all the sergeants and dou-ble-u o ones, Bless all the corp'rals and their blink-in'

sons,'Cos we're say-ing good-bye to them all. As back to their bil-lets they crawl, You'll

get no pro-mo-tion this side of the o-cean, So cheer up, my lads, BLESS 'EM ALL!

D.S. %

Last time

No-bo-dy knows what a twirp you've been, So cheer up, my lads, BLESS 'EM ALL!

A BROKEN DOLL

Words by CLIFFORD HARRIS
Music by JAS W TATE

BYE BYE BLACKBIRD

Words by MORT DIXON
Music by RAY HENDERSON

CAROLINA IN THE MORNING

Words by GUS KAHN
Music by WALTER DONALDSON

Nothing could be finer than to be in Car-o-li-na in the morn -

-ing. No one could be sweeter than my lovely when I meet her in the morn -

-ing. Where the morn-ing glor-ies twine around the door,

Whispering pret - ty stor-ies I long to hear once more.

17

COMRADES

Words and Music
by FELIX McGLENNON

Tempo di Valse

Com - rades, com - rades

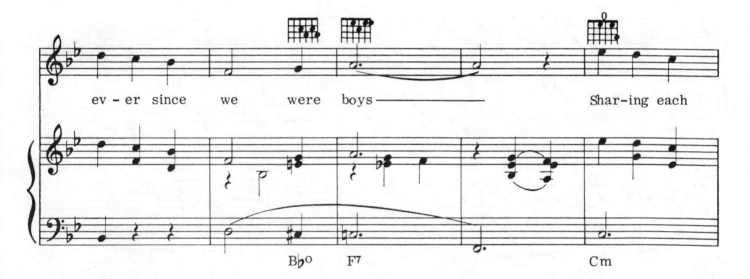

ev - er since we were boys —————— Shar-ing each

Bb° F7 Cm

oth - er's sor - rows, Shar-ing each oth - er's

F7 Bb Gm7 C7

joys ——————— Comrades when manhood was dawn ——

F7   Bb   Eb Ebm Bb

— ing   Faith-ful what - e'er may be - tide —————

Eb   Cm   D7   G7

When dan-ger threatened, my   dar-ling old   com-rade was   there

Cm   E°   Bb   Gm   C7

rall.

by   my   side.—————   side.—————

Eb   F7   Bb   F7   Bb
Ped. F

CONGRATULATIONS

Words and Music by
PHIL COULTER and BILL MARTIN

VERSE

CODA   Slower   *accelerando poco a poco*

Tempo I

DADDY WOULDN'T BUY ME A BOW-WOW

Words and Music by
JOSEPH TABRAR

Daddy would-n't buy me a bow-wow, bow-wow, Daddy would-n't buy me a bow-wow, bow-wow, I've got a lit-tle cat, and I'm ve-ry fond of that, But I'd ra-ther have a bow-wow, wow-wow, wow-wow. -wow.

DA-DAR-DA-DAR (DA-DAR-DA-DEE)

Words by STANLEY DAMERELL and ROBERT HARGREAVES
Music by TOLCHARD EVANS

DAISY BELL

Written and composed
by HARRY DACRE

Dai - sy, Dai - sy,

Give me your an - swer do! ———————— I'm

half cra - zy, All for the love of

DON'T DILLY DALLY
(My Old Man)

Words by CHARLES COLLINS
Music by FRED W LEIGH

My old man said, "Fol-low the van, Don't dil-ly

dal-ly on the way!" Off went the cart with the

home packed in it, I walked be-hind with my old cock

DOWN BY THE OLD MILL STREAM

Words and Music
by TELL TAYLOR

DON'T BRING LULU

Words by BILLY ROSE and LEW BROWN
Music by RAY HENDERSON

Now You can bring Pearl, she's a darn nice girl, but don't bring Lu-lu; You can bring Rose with the turned up nose, but don't bring Lu-lu. Lu-lu al-ways wants to do What we boys don't want her to, Ev-'ry time she starts a-round

Lon-don Bridge is fall - ing down. You can bring cake, or fillets of steak, but

don't bring Lu-lu; Lu-lu gets blue and she goes 'cuck-oo', Like the clock up-on the

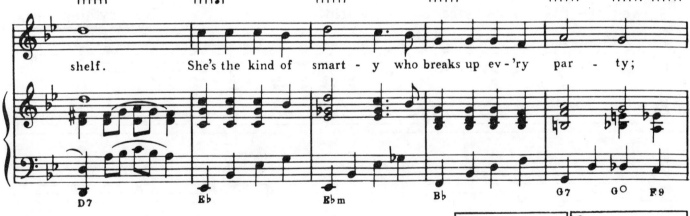

shelf. She's the kind of smart - y who breaks up ev-'ry par - ty;

Hul-la-ba-loo-loo Don't bring Lu-lu. I'll bring her my - self." Now -self." Now -self."

EVERYTHING IS BEAUTIFUL

Words and Music
by RAY STEVENS

DOWN AT THE OLD BULL AND BUSH

Words by ANDREW B STERLING,
RUSSELL and PERCY KRONE
Music by HARRY VON TILZER

FOLLOWING IN FATHER'S FOOTSTEPS

Words and Music
by E W ROGERS

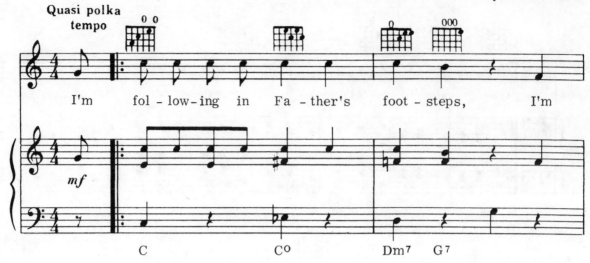

Lyrics (line 1):
I'm fol-low-ing in Fa-ther's foot-steps, I'm fol-low-ing the dear old Dad! He's just in front with a fine big gal, So I thought I'd have one as well! I

Lyrics (line 2):
He's wob-b'ling on in the front, you see, And, 'pon my word, he's worse than me! I

Chord symbols: C C° Dm7 G7 G(9♭) C Gm6 A7 Dm A7 Dm D7 F G7

don't know where he's go - ing, But when he gets there I'll be

C   C⁰   Dm7   G7   G(9♭)

glad!   I'm fol-low-ing in Fa -ther's foot-steps —yes! (hic) I'm

C   C⁰   C7   Fm   F   D7

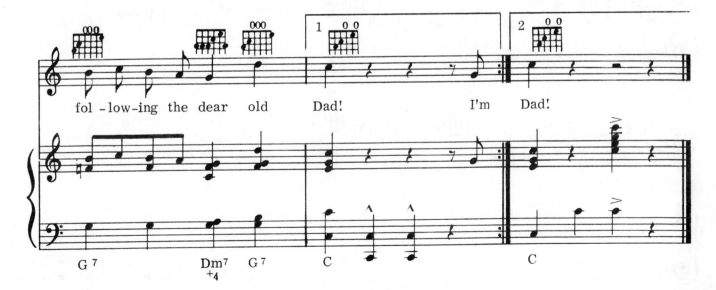

fol -low-ing the dear old Dad!   I'm Dad!

G 7   Dm7   G7   C   C
+4

FOR ME AND MY GAL

Words by EDGAR LESLIE AND E RAY GOETZ
Music by GEO W MEYER

"The bells are ring-ing____ For Me And My Gal,

____ The birds are sing - ing____ For Me And My Gal.____

____ Ev-'ry-bod-y's been know - ing____ To a wed-ding they're go - ing____

____ And for weeks they've been sew - ing,____ Ev-'ry Su - sie and Sal.____

FLANAGAN

Words and Music by
C W MURPHY and WILL LETTERS

GLORIOUS BEER

Words by LEGGETT
Music by WILL GODWIN

GOOD-BYE-EE

Words and Music by
R P WESTON and BERT LEE

THE HONEYSUCKLE AND THE BEE

Words by W PENN
Music by A H FITZ

HELLO DOLLY!

Words and Music
by JERRY HERMAN

HEL - LO, DOL - LY, well, HEL - LO, DOL - LY, It's so nice to have you

back where you be-long. You're look-ing swell, Dol-ly, we can tell,

Dol-ly, You're still glow-in', you're still crow-in', you're still go-in' strong. We feel the room

HOMETOWN

Words and Music by
J KENNEDY and M CARR

50

HAS ANYBODY HERE SEEN KELLY?

Words and Music by
C W MURPHY and WILL LETTERS

This arrangement © 1969 Francis Day & Hunter Ltd, London WC2H 0LD

I LOVE A LASSIE

Words by HARRY LAUDER and GERALD GRAFTON
Music by HARRY LAUDER

This arrangement © 1971 Francis Day & Hunter Ltd, London WC2H 0LD

I'LL BE YOUR SWEETHEART

Words and Music
by HARRY DACRE

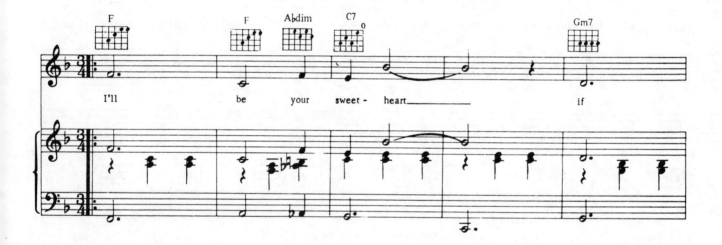

I'll be your sweet - heart _____ if

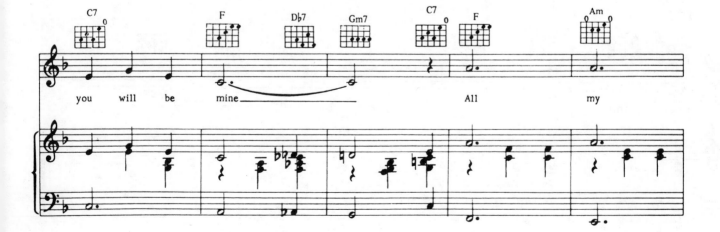

you will be mine _____ All my

IF YOU KNEW SUSIE LIKE I KNOW SUSIE

Words and Music
by B G De SYLVA

If you knew Su-sie like I know Su-sie Oh!

G   C

Oh!   Oh! what a girl!___ There's none so clas-sy as
She wears long tress-es and

C#dim   G7

this fair las-sie   Oh!   Oh!   Ho-ly Mos-es
nice tight dress-es   Oh!   Oh!   What a fu-ture

G+   C

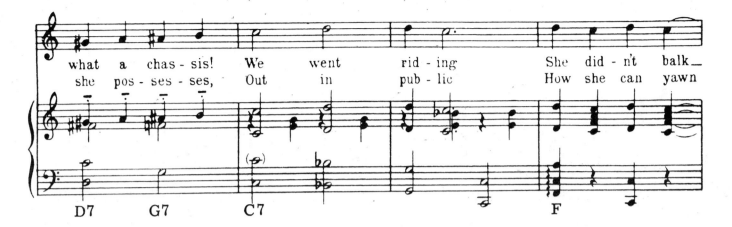

IF YOU WERE THE ONLY GIRL IN THE WORLD

Words by CLIFFORD GREY
Music by NAT D AYER

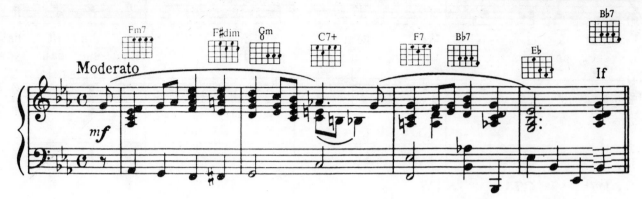

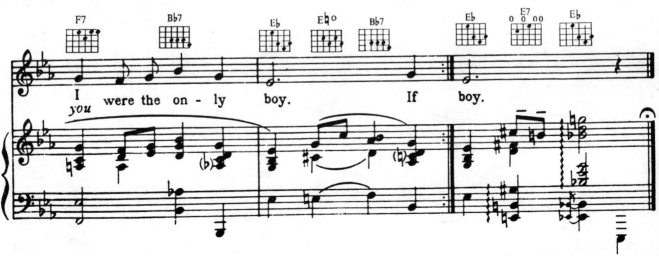

I'LL BE SEEING YOU

Words by IRVING KAHAL
Music by SAMMY FAIN

I'LL GET BY (As Long As I Have You)

Words by ROY TURK
Music by FRED AHLERT

I BELONG TO GLASGOW

Words and Music
by WILL FYFFE

I WOULDN'T LEAVE MY LITTLE WOODEN HUT

Words and Music by
TOM MELLOR and CHAS COLLINS

IF THOSE LIPS COULD ONLY SPEAK

Words and Music by
CHAS RIDGEWELL and WILL GODWIN

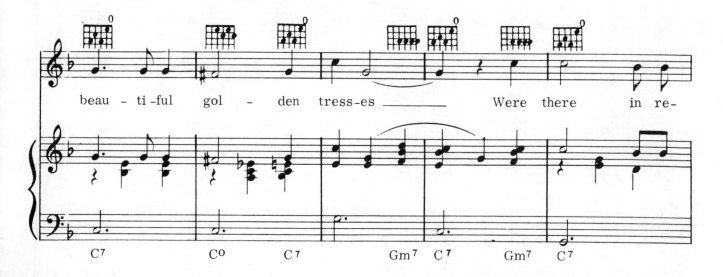

I'M HENERY THE EIGHTH, I AM!

Words and Music
by MURRAY and WESTON

67

I'M SHY MARY ELLEN, I'M SHY

Words and Music by
GEO STEVENS and CHAS RIDGWELL

I'm shy, Ma - ry El - len, I'm shy,

It does seem so naught-y, oh, my! Tho'

kiss - ing is nice I've of - ten heard say, But

still how to do it, I don't know the way. So

I USED TO SIGH FOR THE SILVERY MOON

Words by LESTER BARRATT
Music by HERMANN E DAREWSKI JNR

I WAS A GOOD LITTLE GIRL TILL I MET YOU

Words by CLIFFORD HARRIS
Music by JAMES W TATE

IT'S A GREAT BIG SHAME

Words by EDGAR BATEMAN
Music by GEO Le BRUNN

IN THE TWI-TWI-TWILIGHT

Words and Music by
CHARLES WILMOT and HERMAN DAREWSKI JNR

talk, talk, talk   That's the time they long

for,   Just be-fore the— night.———————— And

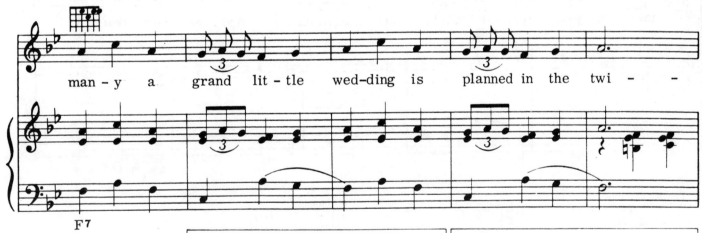

man-y a grand lit-tle wed-ding is planned in the twi--

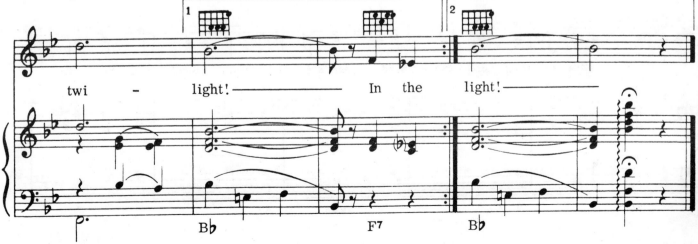

twi - light!——————— In the light!———————

IN THE SHADE OF THE OLD APPLE TREE

Words by HARRY H WILLIAMS
Music by EGBERT VAN ALSTYNE

I WONDER WHERE MY BABY IS TO-NIGHT

Words by GUS KAHN
Music by WALTER DONALDSON

IS IT TRUE WHAT THEY SAY ABOUT DIXIE?

Words and Music by IRVING CAESAR,
SAMMY LERNER and GERALD MARKS

JUST LIKE THE IVY, I'LL CLING TO YOU

Words by A J MILLS
Music by HARRY CASTLING

JOSHU-AH

Words and Music by
GEORGE ARTHURS and BERT LEE

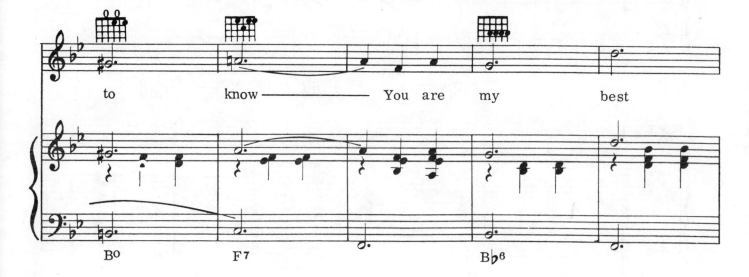

KNEES UP MOTHER BROWN

Words by I PAYTOR
Music by WESTON and LEE

LILY OF LAGUNA

Words and Music
by LESLIE STUART

THE LAMBETH WALK

Words by DOUGLAS FURBER
Music by NOEL GAY

An-y time you're Lam-beth way__ An-y eve-ning an-y day,__ You'll find__ us all do-in' the Lam-beth walk.__ Ev-'ry lit-tle Lam-beth gal__ With her lit-tle Lam-beth pal,__ You'll find__ 'em all do-in' the Lam-beth walk.

LET'S ALL GO DOWN THE STRAND!

Words and Music by
HARRY CASTLING and C W MURPHY

89

LILLI MARLENE

Words by TOMMIE CONNOR
Original Words by HANS LEIP
Music by NORBERT SCHULTZE

Underneath the lantern by the barrack gate, Darling I remember the way you used to wait; 'Twas
Time would come for roll call, time for us to part, Darling I'd caress you and press you to my heart; And

There that you whispered tenderly, That you lov'd me, You'd always be,
There 'neath that far off lantern light, I'd hold you tight, We'd kiss "Good-night;" My Lilli of the

lamplight, My own LIL-LI MAR-LENE.

© 1944 Appolo Verlag (Germany)
Sub-published by Peter Maurice Music Co Ltd, London WC2H 0LD

Or - ders came for sail - ing some-where o - ver there, All con-fined to bar - racks was
Rest-ing in a bill - et just be - hind the line, Ev - en tho' we're part - ed your

C   G7

more than I could bear; I knew you were wait - ing in the street, I heard your feet, But
lips are close to mine; You wait where that lan - tern soft - ly gleams, Your sweet face seems, To

C C7   F   C   G7

could not meet; My Lil - li of the lamp - light, My own LIL - LI MAR-
haunt my dreams,

F   C   Dm7   G7   C   G7

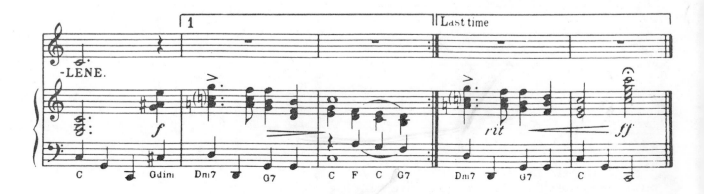

-LENE.

1   Last time

C   Gdim Dm7   G7   C F C G7   Dm7   G7   C

LITTLE ANNIE ROONEY

Words and Music
by MICHAEL NOLAN

She's my sweet-heart I'm her beau

She's my An-nie I'm her Joe Soon

we'll mar-ry nev-er to part Lit-tle An-nie

Roon-ey is my sweet-heart. -heart.

LILY THE PINK

Adapted and Arranged by
GORMAN, McGEAR and McGOUGH

93

LOVE IS THE SWEETEST THING

Words and Music
by RAY NOBLE

95

MAIRZY DOATS AND DOZY DOATS

Words and Music by MILTON DRAKE,
AL HOFFMAN and JERRY LIVINGSTON

Moderato

Mair - zy doats and do - zy doats and lid - dle lam - zy div - ey

kiddle - y div - ey too, would - n't you? Yes! Mair - zy doats and do - zy oats and

lid - dle lam - zy div - ey A kiddle - y div - ey too, wouldn't you? If the

words sound queer, and fun - ny to your ear, a lit - tle bit jumbled and

ME AND MY SHADOW

Words by BILLY ROSE
Music by AL JOLSON and DAVE DREYER

MEET ME TONIGHT IN DREAMLAND

Words by SLATER WHITSON
Music by LEO FRIEDMAN

Meet me to - night in dream - land,

un - der the sil - v'ry moon. ——————— Meet me to -

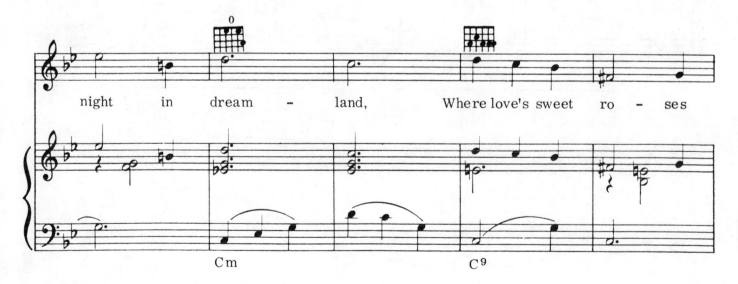

night in dream - land, Where love's sweet ro - ses

MY OLD DUTCH

Words by A C INGLE
Music by C ALBERT CHEVALIER

VERSE

I've got a pal, A reg'lar out an' outer: She's a

dear good old gal, I'll tell yer all about 'er; It's man-y years since fust we met, 'Er

'air was then as black as jet, It's whiter now, but she don't fret, Not my old gal We've

Chorus

been to-geth-er now for for-ty years, An' it don't seem a day too much, There

Eb   Fm7 Bb7 Eb   Eb   F7   Bb

ain't a la-dy liv-in' in the land, As I'd swop for my dear old Dutch, There

Cm   D7   Gm G7 Cm C7   Fm   Bb7   Eb   Bb7

D.C.

ain't a la-dy liv-in' in the land, As I'd swop for my dear old Dutch.

Cm   D7   Gm G7 Cm C7   Fm   Bb7   Eb

NOW IS THE HOUR (Haere Ra)

Words and Music by
CLEMENT SCOTT and MAENA KAIHAU

ON MOTHER KELLY'S DOORSTEP

Words and Music
by GEO A STEVENS

On Mother Kel-ly's door-step, __ down Par-a-dise Row __ I'd sit a-long o'
Nel - ly, __ she'd sit a-long o' Joe. She'd got a lit-tle hole in her frock, hole in her shoe,
Hole in her sock, where her toe peep'd through, But Nel-ly was the smart-est down our

PACK UP YOUR TROUBLES IN YOUR OLD KIT BAG

Words and Music by
GEORGE ASAF and FELIX POWELL

PAPER DOLL

Words and Music
by JOHNNY S BLACK

flir- ty flir- ty eyes, Will have to flirt with dol- lies that are real. When

C   Em7   A7   G7   C7 Cdim C7

I come home at night she will be waiting. She'll be the tru-est doll in all the

F   D7   G7   C7   F   F   D7   G7   C7

world.   I'd rath- er have a pa- per doll to call my own, than have a

A7   Bb   Fdim   F   A7   D7

fick- le min- ded real live girl.   I'm goin' to   girl.

G7   Bbm6   C7   F Fdim C7   F

PRETTY BABY

Words by GUS KAHN
Music by TONY JACKSON and EGBERT VAN ALSTYNE

PUPPET ON A STRING

Words and Music by
PHIL COULTER and BILL MARTIN

VERSE

Love is just like a mer-ry-go-round With all the fun of the fair
I may win on the round-a-bout, Then I lose on the swings

One day I'm feel-ing down on the ground
In or out, there is nev-er a doubt

Then I'm up in the air___ Are you lead-ing me on?___ To-
Just who's pull-ing the strings I'm all tied up in you!___ But

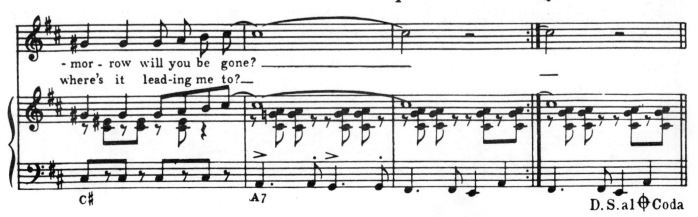

- mor-row will you be gone? _____
where's it lead-ing me to?___

D.S. al ⊕ Coda

CODA

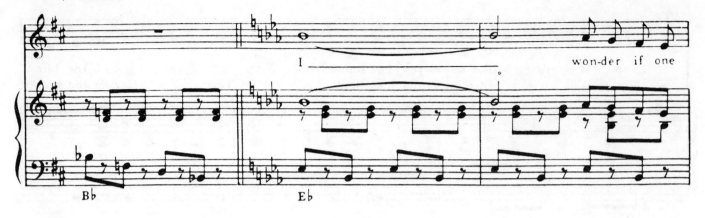

I _____ won-der if one

day that you'll say that you care, If you say you love me mad-ly, I'd glad-ly be

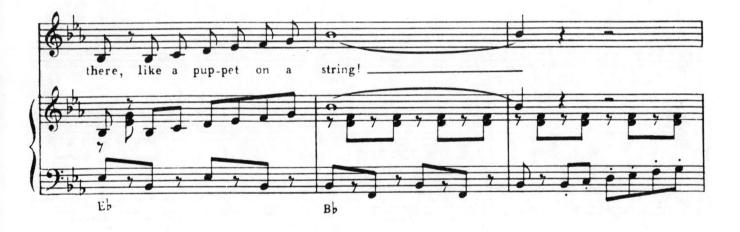

there, like a pup-pet on a string! _____

Like a pup-pet on a string!

MAYBE IT'S BECAUSE I'M A LONDONER

Words and Music
by HUBERT GREGG

NELLIE DEAN

Words and Music
by HARRY ARMSTRONG

ROAMIN' IN THE GLOAMIN'

Words and Music
by HARRY LAUDER

ROLL ME OVER

Words and Music
by DESMOND O'CONNOR

chor-us af-ter me, Roll me ov-er,bless my soul,We're at it a-gain.

A7   D7   G C G

Roll me Ov- er Roll me ov- er Roll me ov-er bless my

D7   G   G7   C   Cm6   G

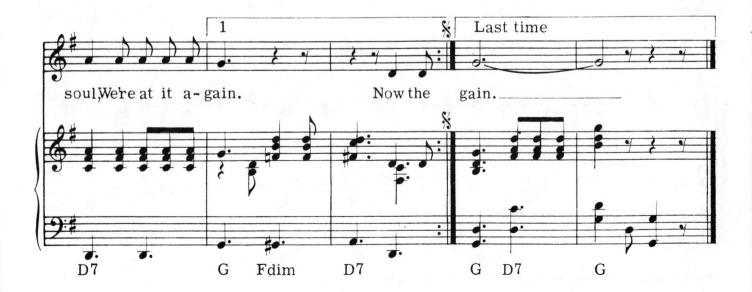

soul,We're at it a-gain.   Now the   gain.

D7   G Fdim D7   G D7   G

ROLLING 'ROUND THE WORLD

Words and Music
by SCOTT SANDERS

Roll-ing round the world   Look-ing for the sun-shine That

nev-er seems to come my   way.   Rolling 'round the

world,   Where ev-'ry lit-tle mill-stone   Seems to look at   me   and

OH! YOU BEAUTIFUL DOLL

Words by A SEYMOUR BROWN
Music by NAT D AYER

If you ev - er leave __ me how my heart will ache, __ I want to hug __ you, but I fear you'd break, __ Oh, oh, oh, oh, Oh, you beau - ti - ful doll! doll!

ROLL OUT THE BARREL

Words and Music by LEW BROWN,
V A TIMM and T VEJVODA

Zing! Boom! Ta - rar - rel _____ Ring out a

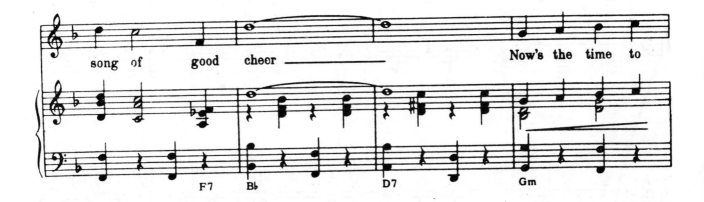

song of good cheer _____ Now's the time to

roll the bar - rel _____ For the gang's all

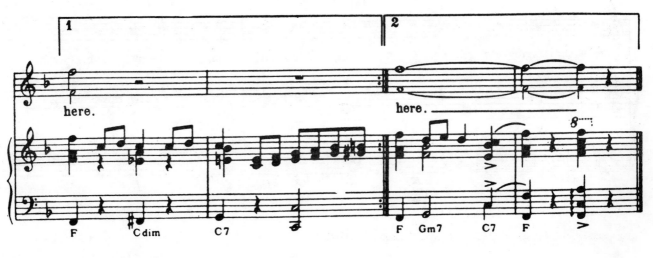

1. here.

2. here. _____

RUN RABBIT RUN!

Words by NOEL GAY and RALPH BUTLER
Music by NOEL GAY

Run, rab-bit, run, rab-bit, run, run, run. Run, rab-bit,

run, rab-bit, run, run, run. Bang, bang, bang, bang,

goes the farm-er's gun, Run, rab-bit, run, rab-bit, run, run,

run. Run, rab-bit, run, rab-bit, run, run, run.

Don't give the farm - er his fun, fun, fun. He'll get

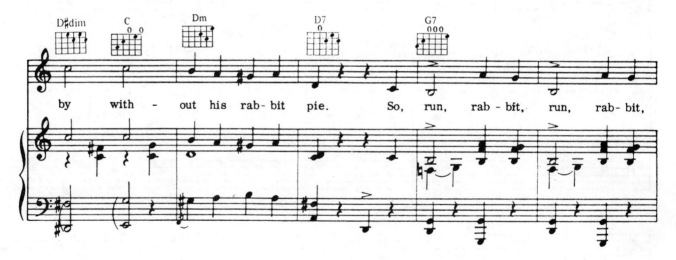

by with - out his rab-bit pie. So, run, rab-bit, run, rab-bit,

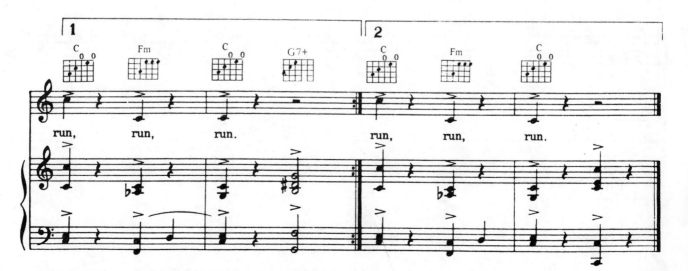

run, run, run. run, run, run.

SALLY

Words and Music by W E HAINES,
HARRY LEON and L TOWERS

blue you're be- guil- ing, _____ When they are grey you're still

C   Ab7

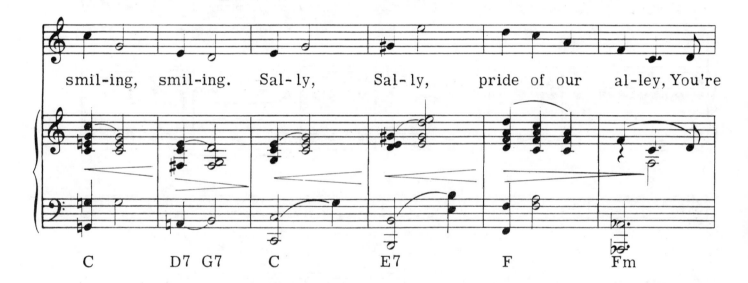

smil-ing, smil-ing. Sal-ly, Sal-ly, pride of our al-ley, You're

C D7 G7 C E7 F Fm

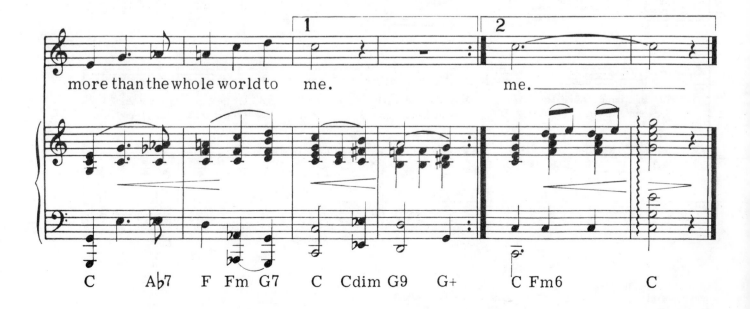

more than the whole world to me.   me. _____

C Ab7 F Fm G7 C Cdim G9 G+ C Fm6   C

SECOND HAND ROSE

Words and Music by
JAMES F HANLEY and GRANT CLARKE

SOMEBODY STOLE MY GIRL

Words and Music
by LEO WOOD

Some-bo-dy stole my gal ——— Some-bo-dy stole my pal. ——— Some-bo-dy came and took her a-way ——— She did-n't ev — en say she was leav — in'. The kiss-es I loved so ———

SOUTH OF THE BORDER

Words and Music by
J KENNEDY and M CARR

South of the Bor - der____ down Mex-i-co way____ Then she sighed as she whispered "Ma - ña - na" Never

Eb   Ab   Bb7   Eb   Eb   Fm

dreaming that we were parting And I lied as I whispered "Ma - ña - na" For our to-mor-row never came. South of the Bor - der____

Bb7   Eb   Eb   C7   Fm   Abm Eb Bb7 Eb   Eb

____ I rode back one day_____ There in a veil of white by can - dle-light she knelt to pray__ The Mission bells

Ab   Bb7   Eb   Ebdim   Bb7

told me____ that I must-n't stay_____ South of the Bor - der____ down Mex-i-co way_____ Ay! Ay! Ay!

Eb   Eb7   Ab   Eb   ♩.   Ab Bb7 Eb

Ay!_____ Ay! Ay! Ay! Ay!_____ Ay! Ay! Ay! Ay!____ Ay! Ay! Ay! Ay!____

Bb7   Eb   Bb7   Eb   Abm   Eb

THE SPANIARD THAT BLIGHTED MY LIFE

Words and Music
by BILLY MERSON

If I catch Al - phon- so Spa - go - ni, the Tor - e - a -

-dor Ah ___ Ah ___ Ah ___ With a might - y swipe I will

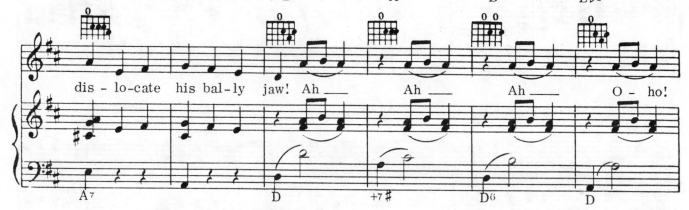

dis - lo - cate his bal - ly jaw! Ah ___ Ah ___ Ah ___ O - ho!

I'll fight this bull - fight-er I will! And when I catch the bound-er, the

SWEET GEORGIA BROWN

Medium tempo

Words and Music by BEN BERNIE,
KENNETH CASEY and MACEO PINKARD

STROLLIN'

Words and Music
by RALPH READER

Stroll - in', _____ just stroll - in', _____ In the cool of the eve - ning air, _____ I don't en - vy the rich- _____ in their au - to - mo - biles, _____ For a mo - tor car is pho - ney, I'd rath - er have shank - s's po - ny When I'm stroll - in', _____

STEIN SONG

Words and Music by
E A FENSTAD and LINCOLN COLCARD

Fill _____ the steins for auld lang syne, Shout till the

raft - ers ring!_____ Stand _____ and drink a

toast once a - gain,___ Let ev - 'ry loy - al voice now sing,___

(Then,) drink _____ to all the hap - py hours,

Drink to the care - less days, _____ Drink ___ to

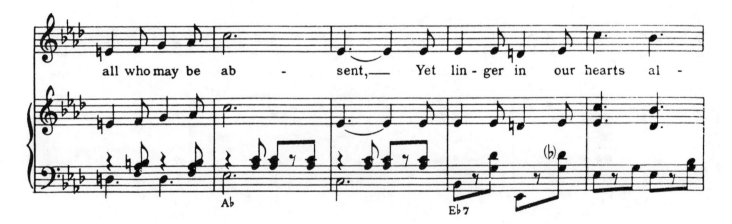

all who may be ab - sent, ___ Yet lin - ger in our hearts al -

1st time - To trio ‖ 2nd time (Finish)

-ways. _____ To the -ways. _____

trees,___ to the sky___ To the Spring in its glo-ri-ous hap-pi-ness, To the

C   Fm   C7   Fm   C7   Fm

youth___ to the fire,___ To the life that is mov-ing and call-ing us; To the

Bb   Eb   Bb7   Eb   Bb7   Eb

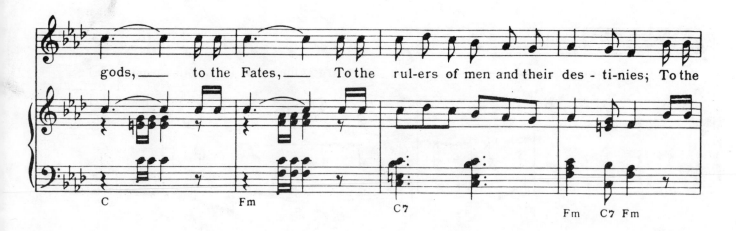

gods,___ to the Fates,___ To the rul-ers of men and their des-ti-nies; To the

C   Fm   C7   Fm   C7   Fm

D. S.

eyes,___ to the lips,___ Of the lass-ies who love us the best;___ Oh,

Bb   Eb   Bb7   Eb   Eb7

SHE WAS ONE OF THE EARLY BIRDS

Words and Music
by T W CONNOR

She was a dear lit-tle dick - ey bird "Chip chip chip" she went ____ Sweet - ly she 'sang' to me, till all my mon-ey was spent! ____ Then she went off song ____ We part-ed on fight - ing terms. ____ She was one of the ear - ly bird and I was one of the worms! ____ worms! ____

SWEET ADELINE

Words by RICHARD H GERARD
Music by HARRY ARMSTRONG

TIE ME KANGAROO DOWN, SPORT

Words and Music
by ROLF HARRIS

THERE IS A TAVERN IN THE TOWN

Traditional

THEY DID'NT BELIEVE ME

Words by M E ROURKE
Music by JEROME D KERN

TWO LITTLE GIRLS IN BLUE

Words and Music
by CHARLES GRAHAM

Two lit-tle girls in blue, lad
Two lit-tle girls in blue, ———— They were
sis-ters, We were bro-thers, And learned to love the

THREE O'CLOCK IN THE MORNING

Words by DOROTHY TERRISS
Music by JULIAN ROBLEDO

It's three o'-clock in the morn- ing, We've danced all the whole night through; And day- light soon will be dawn- ing, Just one more waltz with you. That mel- o- dy so en- tranc- ing, Seems to be made for us two, I could keep danc- ing with you for ev- er, dear, just with you. Its

TWO LOVELY BLACK EYES

Words and Music
by CHARLES COBORN

WAITING AT THE CHURCH

Words by FRED LEIGH
Music by HENRY E PETHER

WHEN IRISH EYES ARE SMILING

Words by CHAUNCEY OLCOTT and GEO GRAFF, Jnr
Music by ERNEST R BALL

When Ir _ ish eyes are smiling, Sure it's like a morn in Spring___ In the

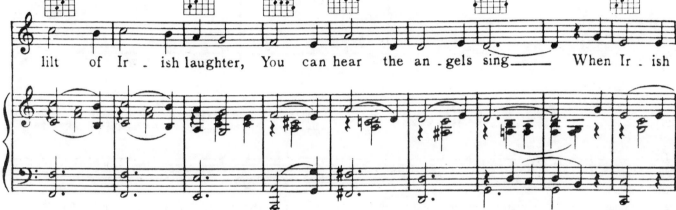

lilt of Ir _ ish laughter, You can hear the an _ gels sing___ When Ir _ ish

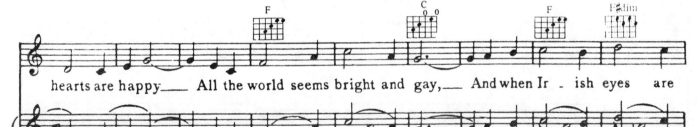

hearts are happy___ All the world seems bright and gay,___ And when Ir _ ish eyes are

smil _ _ ing, Sure they steal your heart a - way. When - way.___

WHEN THE RED, RED ROBIN COMES
BOB, BOB BOBBIN' ALONG

Words and Music
by HARRY WOODS

WHEN IT'S SPRINGTIME IN THE ROCKIES

Words by MARY HALE WOOLSEY
Music by ROBERT SAYER

WHERE DID YOU GET THAT HAT?

Words and Music
by JAMES ROLMAZ

Where did you get that hat? Where did you get that tile? Is-n't it a 'nob-by' one, and just the prop-er style? I should like to have one just the same as that Wher-e'er I go they shout "hel-lo!" Where did you get that tile? tile?

WE ALL GO THE SAME WAY HOME

Words and Music by
C W MURPHY and HARRY CASTLING

WHO'S TAKING YOU HOME TO-NIGHT

Words and Music by
TOMMIE CONNOR and MANNING SHERWIN

Moderate Waltz tempo

Who's tak-ing you home to-night Af-ter the dance is through? _____ Who's go-ing to hold you tight And whis-per "I love you, I do?" _____ Who's the luck-y

WHY AM I ALWAYS THE BRIDESMAID?

Words and Music by
CHARLES COLLINS and FRED W LEIGH

VERSE

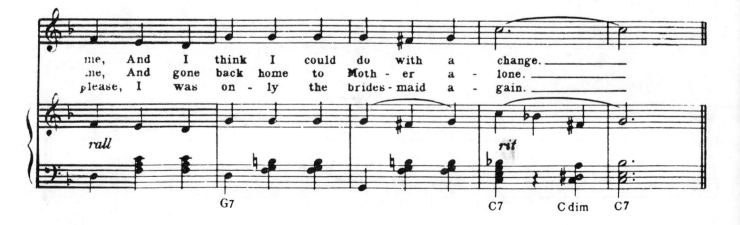

CHORUS

Why am I al-ways the brides - maid, Nev-er the blush-ing bride?____ Ding -

-dong! wed-ding bells On - ly ring for oth-er 'gels', But some fine

day ____ Oh, let it be soon!____ I shall wake up _ in the

morn - ing On my own ____ hon-ey-moon.   -moon. ____

After last verse

WHEN FATHER PAPERED THE PARLOUR

Words and Music
by WESTON and BARNES

YOU WERE MEANT FOR ME

Words by ARTHUR FREED
Music by NACIO HERB BROWN

—You're like a plain-tive mel - o - dy ———————— That

nev - er lets me free ———————— For I'm con -

-tent the an - gels must have sent you and they meant you

just for me. ——————— me. ——— 3 ———

THE WHIFFENPOOF SONG
BAA! BAA! BAA!

Words and Music by MEADE MINNIGERODE,
GEORGE S POMEROY and TODD B GALLOWAY

Printed by Watkiss Studios Ltd., Biggleswade, Beds. 9/92